Get Set Go Phonics

The Three Little Pigs

Phonics Consultant Susan Purcell

Illustrator Sharon Harmer

Concept Fran Bromage

Miles Kelly

Once upon a time, there were three little pink pigs, who lived with their mother, Polly.

Say the names as you spot each pig in the picture.

Pip

Pat

Pam

One day the little pigs, called Pip, Pat and Pam, packed their bags and left home.

Point to the things in the picture that are pink.

Sound out the things in the picture beginning with p as you find them.

petal   pig   pocket   path

The little pigs laid out a rug in the sun and Pam tucked into a bun. "This is all such fun," she said, "but we must find somewhere to live."

Spot the word that doesn't have the u sound.

bus   hut   nut   run   tap

Just then Pip saw a farmer with a horse and cart full of straw. "I could build a house with that," said Pip. "Do you have any more?"

Caw, caw.

Sound out these words with the or sound.

store   chore   adore

jaw   claw   four   pour

5

Pip built his house of straw, but a hungry wolf thought Pip looked like a tasty tit-bit. "Let me in little pig!" said the wolf.

"Not by the hair on my chinny chin chin. I'll not let you in!" said Pip.

Emphasize the i sound as you say this sentence together.

"Not by the hair on my chinny chin chin. I'll not let you in!"

"Then I'll huff and I'll puff and I'll blow your house down," boasted the wolf. And he did!

"No, no!" cried Pip, running away. "I must go!"

Sound out these words, which all use the oa sound.

toad   boat   loaf   ago   so

show   low   tow   crow

Look out for the st blend, as you read aloud

Pat and Pam were **st**ill exploring. Pat found a **st**ack of **st**icks.

"I can build a house with these," he said. "I'll **st**art right now!"

Spot the word that doesn't begin with the st blend.

step   stir   star   slug   stop

Later, Pat heard a tapping at the window. "Let me in little pig!" said the big bad wolf.

"Not by the hair on my chinny chin chin. I'll not let you in," said Pat.

Sound out these words with the a sound in different positions.

tap   cat   flag   that
man   ant   apple

9

As you read, focus on the ow sound (as in down)

"Then I'll huff and I'll puff and I'll blow your house down," said the wolf with a frown. And he did!

Ow, ow!

Which word has the ow sound – brown or yellow?

Sound out these words with the ow sound.

cow   brown   town

proud   scout   cloud

The wolf shouted loudly as sticks clouted his head, and Pat ran out of the way.

Say the words as you spot the flowers in the picture.

blue flowers

yellow flowers

red flowers

Focus on the k sound
made by c and k
(as in stick)

Pam was quick to buy
a stack of bricks to
build her house. She
checked each wall
was strong and thick.

Spot the word that doesn't end with the k sound.

sack   clock   hand   truck

"Beautiful!" said Pam looking back at the building. "Now I'd better go inside and unpack my big bag."

Say the words as you spot things beginning with the b sound.

butterfly

bird

bee

Highlight the ee sound (as in see)

Pam sat down with a cup of tea and looked out of the window. She could see her brothers running past!

"We three must flee," shouted Pip.

Sound out these words with the ee sound.

tree   knee   free

key   ski   pea   sea

Quick as a wink Pip and Pat told Pam about the wolf.

"Hmm, let me think," said Pam, as she drank some tea. "I think I have an idea."

Spot the word that doesn't have **nk** at the end.

pink   went   trunk   blink

Suddenly, the pigs saw the big bad wolf outside in the field. "Let me in little pig!" shouted the wolf.

"Not by the hair on my chinny chin chin. I'll not let you in!" said Pam with a laugh.

"Then I'll huff and I'll puff and I'll blow your house down," said the wolf.

Sound out these words, which all end with the f sound.

graph   leaf   beef

tough   rough   fluff   sniff

16

So he huffed and he puffed,
and he huffed and he puffed.
Inside, the little pigs were
forming a plan.

Spot the word that doesn't begin with the f sound.

face   football   photo   plane

"You won't get far!" shouted the wolf, as he darted onto the roof. "You are trapped," and he started to climb down the chimney.

Sound out these words with the **ar** sound in different positions.

art   arm   arch   card

dark   garden   star   car

But the smart little pigs were on their guard. Pam took charge of boiling a large pot of water under the chimney.

Spot the word that doesn't have the **ar** sound.

jar   hard   pram   cart   park

Suddenly, the wolf dropped at full speed into the pot! Water spurted everywhere and spilt onto the floor.

The wolf gave a gasp of surprise!

Sound out some words beginning with the **sp** sound.

space   spin   spot   spell

spend   spoon   spade

"Hurrah!" said Pam with a **sp**arkle in her eye. "That's **sp**oilt your plan!"

But the wolf couldn't **sp**eak. He **sp**at out some water and **sp**ed out of the door.

Spot the word that doesn't end in the **sp** blend.

wasp   crisp   past   grasp

After that, the three pigs lived a lovely life together in Pam's little brick house.

Spot the word that doesn't begin with the l sound.

leg   lid   ink   leaf   lion

Ask your child to **retell** the story using these key sounds and story images.

pig   straw   sticks

frown   brick   think

huff   smart   spilt

run   bus   fun   cup   nut

his   pig   bit   chin   little

show   toad   blow   loaf

tap   flag   apple   man

bird   bee   bag   big   back

sea   knee   key   ski   tree

field   tough   puff   face

arm   star   cart   park

lid   leaf   little   leg   lion

You've had fun with phonics! Well done.